C000176873

Amelia & Alex Wasiliev
photography by Elisa Watson

PALEO

hardie grant books

CONTENTS

INTRODUCTION

What is Paleo?

The Paleo way of life has been around for a long time, but only in the last couple of years have its benefits been more widely known and its lifestyle practiced.

The Paleo diet restricts processed foods, sugars, grains and dairy products and encourages a simple diet of fresh fruit and vegetables along with proteins and nuts and seeds.

However, the Paleo lifestyle is much more than a diet. It draws on the core values of the lifestyles of our historical ancestors, who ate whole, unprocessed foods, who moved around more than we do, who slept better and had less stress. It is about having a conscious awareness of the food that we put into our bodies and the effect it has on our bodies. It is also about making healthy choices for our bodies in all areas of our lives, so prioritising good sleeping habits, exercising regularly and working to reduce stress are all equally as important for optimum health.

Why eat Paleo?

This is a fairly simple question to answer. Eating Paleo means your diet and your body will be free of additives, preservatives, chemicals and unwanted toxins. You will eat more fresh fruit and vegetables, which in turn increases the antioxidants and anti-inflammatory benefits to your body. You will eat more red meats and proteins, which will increase the iron your body absorbs.

In essence, you won't be eating anything that has bad properties. This means your body will be able to run efficiently, heal itself and function to its full potential. Here are some of the main reported benefits of a Paleo lifestyle:

- improved gut health
- improved nutrient absorption
- weight loss
- muscle growth
- better sleep
- stabilises blood sugar (known to cure Type 2 diabetes)
- healthy skin
- increased brain function
- increased energy levels
- higher immune function
- less risk of heart disease and cancer
- reduces allergies

7

WHAT SHOULD I EAT?

Foods to Avoid

 Sugar & artificial sweeteners

 Processed foods of any kind: *including ready meals & junk food*

 Grains and cereals of any kind: *flour, rice, rye, barley, corn &oats*

 Legumes, beans, lentils, soy & peanuts

 Processed meats

 Processed vegetable oils

 Dairy products

 Potatoes: *high in starch and low in other nutrients*

 Soft drinks, energy drinks & alcohol

 Coffee: *the high caffeine stimulates your nervous system and can affect sleeping pattern and moods*

 Fruit juices

 Milk & white chocolate & sweets

Foods to Eat with Balance

 Butter: *although it is a dairy product, butter is accepted by most Paleo standards as it is an animal fat. Eat as your body allows.*

 Salt: *should be used in moderation in cooking.*

 Root vegetables: *such as sweet potato, beetroot, turnips and parsnips can all be eaten; however, they are high in carbohydrates and so sugars. If trying Paleo to lose weight, eat them in moderation.*

 Natural sweeteners: *maple syrup and raw honey are the best to use when eating a Paleo diet as they are unprocessed. They are still very* high in fructose and sucrose so best to use moderately.

Dried fruit: *dates, apricots, sultanas, pineapple, etc. Any dried fruit has a much higher fructose content than fresh. Only eat occasionally to avoid high sugar spikes and buy naturally dried products.*

 Nowadays a lot of your favourite sauces and dressings have sugar-free alternatives. Always check the labels. Make sure there are as few ingredients as possible and no added sugar.

Foods to Eat/Embrace

 Meat & animal products: *beef, venison, lamb, duck and chicken. Unprocessed grass-fed meats from all animal types as well as animal products such as gelatine.*

 Fish and seafood

 Fresh vegetables: *leafy greens, carrot, celery, kale, cauliflower, aubergine, onions, leeks, garlic, salad vegetables and herbs, such as parsley.*

 Fresh fruits: *berries, apples, pears, mangoes, avocados; the list goes on.*

 Organic eggs

 Nuts: *almonds, cashews, pecans, hazelnuts and macadamia nuts. All nuts that are going to be eaten should be 'activated'. This process removes the enzyme inhibitors of nuts and allows the body to break them down more easily. You can buy nuts already activated or you can do it at home.*

To activate nuts: Put about 150g nuts in a large bowl and pour in enough water to cover. Add 1 teaspoon salt and stir until the salt is dissolved. Soak for 12 hours, then drain, rinse and dry thoroughly.

 Seeds: *pumpkin seeds, sunflower, chia, flaxseed and sesame seeds.*

 Natural healthy oils: *olive oil, nuts oil (except groundnut/peanut as it's a legume), avocado oil, sesame oil and fruit oils such as avocado oil.*

 Coconut oil: *a rich source of healthy, saturated fatty acids, well-suited to the Paleo diet.*

 Animal fats, lard & ghee: *great alternatives to vegetable oils when needed. They will fry at higher temperatures and there is no need to feel guilty about eating them.*

 Coconut milk & cream: *great as a dairy alternative and can be used in smoothies, sweets and curries.*

 Fermented foods: *excellent for digestion, as they contain natural healthy bacteria. Eat plenty of them but make sure that there is no added sugar. The best products are lacto-fermented products which are usually just fermented in salty water, such as the Mixed Pickled Vegetables (p. 70).*

 Sea vegetables: *dulse, nori and wakame.*

 Flour alternatives: *coconut flour, ground almonds, tapioca flour, arrowroot and chia seed flour are great alternatives to grain flours.*

 Vinegars: *avoid malt and barley vinegars as they contain gluten, but choose fermented vinegars made from fruit, such as apple cider vinegar, red and white wine vinegars and balsamic.*

HOW TO START YOUR PALEO LIFESTYLE

It doesn't take much to begin the Paleo way of life. Clean out your fridge and storecupboard and spend an afternoon preparing some of the basic recipes in this book. If you need a little more inspiration, use the following menu plans to create your weekly shopping list. One thing is for sure, you won't be hungry! The Paleo lifestyle has no limit to the amount of food you eat, so choose a couple of snacks each day if you need them. After the first week, you will find that if you eat well at mealtimes you probably won't need snacks anyway.

MENU PLAN: WEEK 1

DAY 1:
Breakfast: *Scrambled Eggs with Bacon (p.52)*
Lunch: *Roasted Beetroot & Rocket Salad (p.92)*
Dinner: *Bangers & Sweet Potato Mash (p.128)*
with Chinese Broccoli with Almonds (p.102)
Snacks: *fresh fruit, Guacamole (p.76)*
with Chia Seed Crackers (p.62)

DAY 2:
Breakfast: *Almond Milk Banana Smoothie (p.46)*
Lunch: *leftover Chinese Broccoli with*
Almonds (p.102) and Chorizo Balls (p.68)
Dinner: *Mediterranean Lamb (p.130)*
Snacks: *Spiced Nuts (p.64), chopped raw vegetables,*
(carrots, celery, cucumber)

DAY 3:
Breakfast: *Breakfast Waffles (p.48)*
Lunch: *leftover Mediterranean Lamb (p.130)*
with fresh rocket or spinach
Dinner: *Wild Fish with Salsa Verde (p.144)*
Snacks: *Nut Energy Bars (p.152),*
leftover Chorizo Balls (p.68)

DAY 4:
Breakfast: *Bacon & Egg Breakfast Cups (p.44)*
Lunch: *Chicken Coleslaw (p.100)*
Dinner: *Caveman Burger (p.118)*
Snacks: *fresh fruit, Nut Energy Bars (p.152)*

DAY 5:
Breakfast: *Green Smoothie (p.42)*
Lunch: *Courgette Fritters (p.66) with*
Brussels Sprouts with Bacon (p.90)
Dinner: *Paleo Lasagne (p.134)*
Dessert: *Roasted Peach Crumble (p.156)*
Snack: *Bacon & Egg Breakfast Cups (p.44)*

DAY 6: LEFTOVERS DAY
Breakfast: *leftover Roasted Peach*
Crumble (p.156)
Lunch: *leftover Paleo Lasagne (p.134)*
Dinner: *leftover Courgette Fritters (p.66) with*
Green Salad with Tahini Dressing (p.86)
Snacks: *Nut Energy Bars (p.152),*
Chia Seed Crackers (p.62)

DAY 7:
Breakfast: *Egg with Kale & Aubergine*
Hash (p.38)
Lunch: *Buffalo Wings (p.60) with Spring*
Onion Carrot Noodles (p.84)
Dinner: *Mushroom & Leek Soup (p.140)*
Snack: *Spiced Nuts (p. 64), fresh fruit*

MENU PLAN: WEEK 2

DAY 1:
Breakfast: *Blueberry Chia Pudding (p.40)*
Lunch: *Paleo Bread (p.22) open sandwich*
(choose your own toppings – my favourites include
avocado, smoked fish, tomatoes and fresh herbs)
with leftover Mushroom & Leek Soup (p.140)
Dinner: *Scallops with Parsnip Purée (p.108)*
and leftover Spring Onion Carrot Noodles (p.84)
Snacks: *Sweet Potato & Sumac Fries (p.96)*

DAY 2:
Breakfast: *Apple Cinnamon French Toast (p.56)*
Lunch: *Whole Roasted Mushrooms (p.98)*
with Pumpkin with Cashew Cheese (p.88)
Dinner: *Rib-Eye Steaks with Minty Peas (p.122)*
Snack: *Baba Ganoush (p.78) with raw*
chopped vegetables

DAY 3:
Breakfast: *Breakfast Omelette (p.50)*
Lunch: *Asian-Style Duck Salad (p.94)*
Dinner: *Whole Baked Snapper (p.110) with*
Honey-Roasted Baby Carrots (p.82)
Snack: *Chia Seed Crackers (p.62) with*
Cashew Cheese (p.30)

DAY 4:
Breakfast: *Green Smoothie (p.42)*
Lunch: *leftover Snapper (p.110) with Baba*
Ganoush (p.78) on Paleo Bread (p.22)
Dinner: *Courgette Bolognese (p.132)*
Snack: *Nut Energy Bars (p.152)*

DAY 5:
Breakfast: *Egg with Soldiers (p.54)*
Lunch: *leftover Courgette Bolognese (p.132)*
Dinner: *Poule au Pot (p.114)*
Dessert: *Paleo Chocolate Brownie (p.150)*
Snack: *Nutty Raspberry Friand Bites (p.148)*

DAY 6: LEFTOVERS DAY
Breakfast: *leftover Paleo Bread (p.22) with your*
choice of topping (pure nut butters are
a good breakfast option)
Lunch: *leftover Poule au Pot (p.114)*
Dinner: *Sashimi Salad (p.104)*
Snack: *Paleo Chocolate Brownie (p.150)*

DAY 7:
Breakfast: *Egg with Kale & Aubergine*
Hash (p.38)
Lunch: *Cauliflower Fried Rice (p.124)*
Dinner: *Butternut Squash Gnocchi (p.142)*
Snack: *Spiced Nuts (p.64)*

Using up leftovers

I try to allow for using leftovers for the next day's meals. Once a week, have a leftovers day and give yourself a break from cooking. Don't forget, you can add as much fresh fruit, vegetables, nuts and seeds to your daily intake as you need.

Note to dieters

If you have chosen to use the Paleo lifestyle as a way to lose weight (which you undoubtedly will) it is best to limit your intake of high-fructose fruits. Fresh fruits such as grapes, pineapples, apples, bananas, cherries and pears are high in fructose – although it is natural sugar, it will still play havoc with your body's sugar levels. If losing weight is a priority, try to eat fewer dried fruits and root vegetables as well.

BASICS

Make these recipes in large quantities and keep on hand to add flavour and extra goodness to your Paleo diet. These basics will also help you to convert your usual favourite recipes to a Paleo-friendly version.

Chicken Stock • Simple Salad Vinaigrette
Creamy Tahini Dressing • BBQ Sauce • Paleo
Bread • Chilli Sambal • Paleo Tomato Sauce
Paleo Mayo • Cashew Cheese • Paleo Onion Jam
Cauliflower White Sauce

CHICKEN STOCK

Makes: about 2 litres

YOU NEED
2 onions, unpeeled and roughly chopped • 2 celery sticks, roughly chopped
2 medium carrots, roughly chopped • 1 garlic bulb, unpeeled and cut in half
2 rosemary sprigs • 2 thyme sprigs • 1 tablespoon coconut oil or olive oil • salt
1 whole free-range chicken (can be swapped for other meats or fish
for different stocks)

This nutritious stock is high in vitamin B, zinc, phosphorus and
protein to help strengthen bones and teeth.

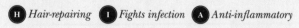

H *Hair-repairing* **I** *Fights infection* **A** *Anti-inflammatory*

In a large pan, heat the vegetables, herbs, half the oil and seasoning over a
medium heat for 7–10 minutes until browned. Rub the remaining oil and salt over
the chicken then place it, skin side down, in the centre of the pan. Cook until
caramelised. Pour in enough water to cover the chicken. Bring to the boil. Cover
and simmer for 2 hours, skimming off any fat that rises to the top. Strain, reserving
the liquid. Store in the refrigerator for 3–4 days or in the freezer for 4–6 months.

SIMPLE SALAD VINAIGRETTE

Makes: about 250 ml

YOU NEED

150 ml olive oil or your oil of choice (e.g. macadamia or avocado oil)

3 tablespoons apple cider vinegar • juice of ½ lemon

1 teaspoon wholegrain mustard • salt and freshly ground black pepper

Rich in monounsaturated fats and high in fibre to help balance blood sugar levels.

Ⓓ *Aids digestion*   Ⓗ *Heart support*   Ⓐ *Anti-inflammatory*

Place all of the ingredients in a jar with a screw-top lid. Shake well to combine.
Taste and adjust seasoning as needed. Store in the refrigerator for up to 2 weeks.

CREAMY TAHINI DRESSING

Makes: about 250 ml

YOU NEED

2 handfuls of baby spinach leaves (or flat-leaf parsley, basil or dill)

100 ml tahini paste • juice of 2 large lemons

1 garlic clove, finely diced • salt and freshly ground black pepper

10 minutes

A great source of calcium, magnesium and phosphorus to help strengthen bones and keep the skin healthy.

E *Energy-boosting*   **H** *Heart support*   **B** *Lowers blood pressure*

Mix all of the ingredients with 100 ml of water in a blender or food processor until smooth. Taste and add more seasoning or lemon juice, if necessary. Add more water to achieve the desired consistency. Transfer to a jar and store in the refrigerator for up to 2 weeks.

BBQ SAUCE

Makes: about 250 ml

YOU NEED

1 small aubergine, cubed • ½ red pepper, diced • 1 small onion, diced

½ tablespoon coconut oil • ½ tablespoon chilli flakes • 60 ml maple syrup

1 tablespoon balsamic vinegar • salt • 125 ml Paleo Tomato Sauce (see page 26)

40 minutes

The aubergine is high in fibre, low in calories and a good source
of B vitamins, while the onion contains sulphur, which is good for a healthy heart.

I *Boosts immunity*   **A** *Anti-inflammatory*   **C** *Lowers cholesterol*

Preheat the oven to 180°C/350°F/Gas 4. Toss the aubergine, red pepper and onion
in the coconut oil and sprinkle with the chilli flakes. Pour in the maple syrup and
vinegar. Season and cook for 30 minutes until roasted. Cool. Blitz the Paleo Tomato
Sauce with the roasted ingredients in a food processor or blender until smooth.
Add water to loosen, if necessary. Strain to achieve an even finer texture, if desired.

PALEO BREAD

Makes: 1 small loaf

YOU NEED

120 g ground almonds • 5 organic eggs • 1 courgette, grated

4 tablespoons coconut oil • 4 tablespoons coconut flour

4 tablespoons LSA (ground linseeds, sunflower seeds, almonds)

2 tablespoons chia seeds, plus extra for topping • 2 tablespoons sesame seeds, plus

extra for topping • 1 tablespoon apple cider vinegar

1 teaspoon bicarbonate of soda

Full of fibre and helps to keep the brain and heart healthy.

B *Strengthens bones*   **E** *Eye protection*   **C** *Lowers cholesterol*

Preheat oven to 160°C/325°F/Gas 3. Grease and line a small (10 × 22cm) loaf tin
with baking paper. Combine all of the ingredients except the extra seeds in a bowl –
it will form quite a runny batter. Transfer to the tin, smooth the top and sprinkle
with the sesame and chia seeds. Bake for 40–45 minutes until a skewer inserted
into the centre comes out clean. Remove from the tin and serve.
Store in an airtight container for 4–5 days.

CHILLI SAMBAL

Makes: about 150 ml

YOU NEED

1 teaspoon sesame oil • 5 fresh cayenne chillies, diced • 4 garlic cloves, finely sliced
15 g piece ginger, peeled and finely diced • 1 lemongrass stalk, crushed
½ teaspoon salt • 60 ml red wine vinegar • juice of 1 lime

24

Chilli can help to boost metabolism, improve digestion, help to clear
sinus congestion and may be able to relieve joint pain.

 A *Anti-inflammatory*   **I** *Boosts immunity*   **C** *Lowers cholesterol*

Heat the oil in a pan over a high heat. Add the chillies, garlic, ginger, lemongrass
and salt and stir to combine. Pour in the vinegar and lime juice. Once simmering,
lower the heat and cook for 15–20 minutes until the liquid has reduced. Cool. Leave
the sauce as it is or blend to a more sauce-like consistency.
Store in an airtight jar for up to 2 weeks.

PALEO TOMATO SAUCE

Makes: about 250 ml

YOU NEED

3 ripe tomatoes • 3 large garlic cloves, peeled • 4–5 shallots

2 tablespoons coconut oil, melted • 250 ml passata • 60 ml red wine vinegar

1 handful of parsley, chopped • salt

Tomatoes are full of antioxidants, beta-carotene and vitamin C to help keep the cardiovascular system healthy.

B *Strengthens bones* **D** *Aids digestion* **B** *Lowers blood pressure*

Preheat the oven to 200°C/400°F/Gas 6. Combine the tomatoes, garlic and shallots in a baking dish. Add the oil, vinegar and a pinch of salt and bake for 15 minutes until the shallots and garlic have softened and the vinegar has reduced. Blitz in a food processer or blender with the passata and 250 ml of water until smooth. Season. Pour into a pan, add the parsley and simmer for 20–25 minutes. Strain for a smoother texture, if desired. Cool, then store in the refrigerator for 2–3 weeks.

PALEO MAYO

Makes: about 250 ml

YOU NEED

3 organic egg yolks • 1 spring onion, finely diced

1 small garlic clove, finely diced • 1 teaspoon Dijon mustard

½ teaspoon raw honey • 250 ml light olive oil

½ teaspoon red wine vinegar • salt • lemon juice (optional)

Rich in vitamins A and D to help keep the eyes healthy and improve night vision.

A *Anti-inflammatory*   **H** *Heart support*   **B** *Strengthens bones*

Combine the egg yolks, spring onion, garlic, mustard and honey and mix on
medium speed in a food processor for 1 minute. While the food processor is on,
slowly drizzle in the oil, a little at a time, allowing the ingredients to combine until
the mixture has a thick, creamy consistency. Taste and add salt, vinegar
and lemon juice, if using. Store in the refrigerator in an airtight jar for 2 weeks.

CASHEW CHEESE

Makes: about 200 g

YOU NEED
150 g cashew nuts • 2 garlic cloves, roasted • 1 teaspoon sea salt
juice of 1 lemon • 1 bunch of chives, finely chopped

Cashews are packed with monounsaturated fats to keep the heart
healthy and help to lower cholesterol.

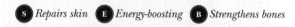

S *Repairs skin* **E** *Energy-boosting* **B** *Strengthens bones*

Soak the cashew nuts in water for 2–3 hours. Drain, rinse well and rub dry with
kitchen paper. Put in a food processor with the garlic, salt and lemon juice
and blend into a grainy paste. Transfer to a bowl, cover and chill for 1–2 hours until
set. Remove from the bowl and roll the edges in chives to serve.
Store in the refrigerator for 4–5 days.

PALEO ONION JAM

Makes: about 250 ml

YOU NEED

2 tablespoons coconut oil • 2 tablespoons organic butter

2 large red onions, cut into thin rings • salt • 2 tablespoons red wine vinegar

3 tablespoons sugar-free strawberry jam

Red onions are a good source of vitamin C and can help to regulate blood sugar levels as well as lower blood pressure.

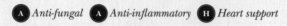

A *Anti-fungal* **A** *Anti-inflammatory* **H** *Heart support*

Heat the oil and butter in a pan over a low heat until the butter has melted. Add the onions and cook for 10 minutes until softened and translucent. Season with salt and stir through. Add vinegar and jam and cook, stirring for 10–15 minutes until the onions soften and thicken. Cool and keep in the refrigerator for up to 2 weeks.

CAULIFLOWER WHITE SAUCE

Makes: about 375 ml

YOU NEED

2 tablespoons olive oil • 2 small shallots, roughly chopped

2 garlic cloves, roughly chopped • 80 g ghee • ½ cauliflower, roughly chopped

500 ml Chicken Stock (see page 14) • 3 basil sprigs with leaves • salt

Cauliflower contains lots of vitamins C and K to help keep the cardiovascular system healthy.

D *Detoxifying*   **A** *Anti-inflammatory*   **D** *Aids digestion*

Heat the oil in a pan over a medium heat. Cook the shallots, garlic and 25 g of the ghee for 7 minutes until softened. Add the cauliflower, season and cook for 4–5 minutes until the cauliflower has browned. Add the stock and basil. Cover and bring to the boil. Simmer for 10–15 minutes. Remove the basil, strain and discard the liquid. Blitz the cauliflower mixture with the remaining ghee and a pinch of salt in a food processor until smooth.

BREAKFAST & BRUNCH

Who doesn't love a cooked breakfast? The Paleo lifestyle is excellent for the cooked breakfast lover – whether you stick to simple eggs and bacon or try something more creative.
Most of your favourites can be converted to be Paleo-friendly. If you're short on time in the morning, try a quick and delicious smoothie.

Egg with Kale & Aubergine Hash
Blueberry Chia Pudding • Green Smoothie
Bacon & Egg Breakfast Cups • Almond Milk
Banana Smoothie • Breakfast Waffles • Breakfast
Omelette • Scrambled Eggs with Bacon • Eggs
with Soldiers • Apple Cinnamon French Toast

EGG WITH KALE & AUBERGINE HASH

Serves: 1

YOU NEED

1½ tablespoons pine nuts • 1 tablespoon coconut oil

½ shallot, finely diced • 1 baby aubergine, diced • ½ courgette, diced

salt • 2 stalks curly kale, leaves finely shredded

1 tablespoon apple cider vinegar • 1 organic egg

25 minutes

Rich in antioxidants and calcium to help keep the joints and cartilage healthy.

B *Strengthens bones* A *Anti-inflammatory* D *Detoxifying*

Toast the pine nuts in a dry frying pan over a medium heat for a few minutes. Set aside. Heat half the oil in a pan and sauté the shallots for 5 minutes. Add the aubergine and courgette and season with salt to taste. Cook, stirring, until the vegetables brown. Add the kale and vinegar and cook for 2–3 minutes. Spoon the hash onto a plate. Fry the egg in the remaining oil and put on top of the hash.

BLUEBERRY CHIA PUDDING

Serves: 2

YOU NEED

100 ml coconut milk (or any nut milk) • 2 tablespoons chia seeds
seeds of 1 vanilla pod • 1 tablespoon maple syrup (optional)
2 teaspoons toasted pumpkin seeds • 2 small handfuls of fresh blueberries

Blueberries are high in fibre and vitamin E to reduce the risk of heart disease and help maintain healthy blood pressure.

 **B** *Regulates blood pressure* **E** *Eye protection* **C** *Lowers cholesterol*

Whisk together 2 tablespoons of water with the coconut milk, chia seeds, vanilla seeds and maple syrup, if using. Set aside for 5 minutes, then whisk to make sure the chia seeds are dispersed. Add 1 handful of berries and mix well.
Put into 2 small bowls, cover and chill for 2 hours, or until set.
Top with the remaining berries and pumpkin seeds.

GREEN SMOOTHIE

Serves: 1 / Makes: 250 ml

YOU NEED

150 g fresh or frozen pineapple • 2 handfuls of baby spinach • 1 orange, peeled
60 ml coconut cream • 2 stalks curly kale, leaves removed • ½ avocado

Dark leafy greens are rich in vitamins A, C and K as well as calcium, potassium and folate and can help boost the immune system.

 Anti-inflammatory   *Detoxifying*   (H) *Heart support*

Blend all of the ingredients in a blender until smooth. Add 60–120 ml of water, depending on desired consistency, and blend until combined. Serve immediately.

BACON & EGG BREAKFAST CUPS

Makes: 8

YOU NEED

coconut oil or butter, for greasing • 8 rashers streaky grass-fed bacon
8 organic eggs • 1 teaspoon chilli flakes • 1 teaspoon black sesame seeds
salt and freshly ground black pepper • 2 spring onions, finely sliced

Bacon is packed with choline, to help with memory, and vitamin B12, which is important for keeping red blood cells healthy.

E *Energy-boosting* **B** *Brain-boosting* **B** *Strengthens bones*

Preheat the oven to 200°C/400°F/Gas 6. Grease a 12-hole muffin tin. Line the base and sides of 8 of the holes with bacon, then bake for 10–15 minutes until it starts to brown and crisp. In a bowl, combine the chilli flakes, sesame seeds and salt and pepper. Break an egg into each bacon-lined hole. Sprinkle with the chilli mixture and bake for 7–8 minutes until the yolk is cooked to your preference. Top with spring onion. Serve immediately or store in the refrigerator for up to 4 days.

ALMOND MILK BANANA SMOOTHIE

Serves: 1 / Makes: 250 ml

YOU NEED
150 ml almond milk • 1 banana • 2 pitted Medjool dates • 1 tablespoon honey

5 minutes

High in calcium, potassium and vitamin E and low in fat to help build strong muscles and keep the heart healthy.

B *Strengthens bones* **S** *Repairs skin* **B** *Lowers blood pressure*

Blend all of the ingredients in a blender until smooth, adding water to thin to desired consistency, if necessary. Serve immediately.

BREAKFAST WAFFLES

Makes: 6–8

YOU NEED

180 g ground almonds • 3 tablespoons coconut flour • 3 tablespoons tapioca flour
1½ tablespoons baking powder • 75 g organic butter, melted, plus extra for greasing
3 organic eggs, lightly beaten • 150 ml almond milk • 1 banana, sliced
1 handful of toasted chopped nuts

High in fibre and promotes heart health including helping
to maintain normal blood pressure.

S *Repairs skin* **D** *Aids digestion* **E** *Energy-boosting*

Combine the ground almonds, coconut flour, tapioca flour and baking powder in
a bowl. In a jug, combine the melted butter, eggs and almond milk. Pour the wet
ingredients into the dry and stir. Set aside for 20 minutes, then pour in 80 ml of
water and stir. Grease and heat a waffle iron or griddle pan and cook each waffle for
6–7 minutes until golden brown and crisp. Top with the banana and nuts and serve.

BREAKFAST OMELETTE

Serves: 1

YOU NEED
3 organic eggs • 50 ml coconut cream

10 g flat-leaf parsley, finely chopped • 2 spring onions, sliced

100 g hot smoked salmon, torn into bite-sized pieces

1 tablespoon coconut or olive oil • 1 tablespoon capers

Full of good fats and helps to strengthen the immune system
and keep the brain healthy.

H *Heart support*   **E** *Eye protection*   **M** *Aids memory*

Beat the eggs, coconut cream and 20 ml of water together. Add the parsley, spring
onion and salmon and mix well. Heat the oil in a frying pan over a medium heat.
Pour in the egg mixture and let the egg begin to set. Sprinkle the capers on top,
then move the egg around to let it cook and set all over. When the top is set,
flip one side of the omelette onto the other and serve immediately.

SCRAMBLED EGGS WITH BACON

Serves: 1

YOU NEED

1 rasher grass-fed bacon, cut in half • 6–8 cherry tomatoes on the vine
2 organic eggs • ½ tablespoon coconut oil • salt
Chilli Sambal (see page 24) (optional)

30 minutes

High in protein and rich in antioxidants, vitamin B and choline, which is important for keeping cells healthy.

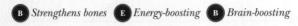

B *Strengthens bones*   **E** *Energy-boosting*   **B** *Brain-boosting*

Preheat the oven to 200°C/400°F/Gas 6. Place the bacon in a baking dish and bake for 10 minutes. Turn the bacon over and add the tomatoes. Bake for 5–10 minutes. Whisk the eggs and 20 ml of water together. Heat the oil in a frying pan over a low heat. Add the eggs, season and cook slowly to your liking. Serve with the bacon, tomatoes and chilli sambal, if using.

EGGS WITH SOLDIERS

Serves: 1

YOU NEED

2 organic eggs • 6–8 asparagus stalks, trimmed • avocado oil, for drizzling

salt and freshly ground black pepper

Asparagus is packed with vitamins A, C, E and K and is a good source of fibre to help protect against heart disease and boost the immune system.

A *Anti-inflammatory* **B** *Brain-boosting* **B** *Strengthens bones*

Bring a full small pan of water to the boil. Carefully place the eggs into the water and boil for 5 minutes. Remove from the pan with a slotted spoon and run under cold water. Drop the asparagus into the boiling water for 1–2 minutes. Drain, drizzle with oil and season. Peel or cut the top off the eggs and serve with asparagus.

55

APPLE CINNAMON FRENCH TOAST

Serves: 1

YOU NEED

1 green apple, peeled and thinly sliced • 20 g organic butter

½ teaspoon ground cinnamon • 2 slices of Paleo Bread (see page 22)

1 organic egg, lightly beaten • maple syrup (optional)

High in antioxidants, fibre and can help to lower cholesterol.

H *Heart support* **B** *Brain-boosting* **B** *Regulates blood sugar*

Heat the apples and half the butter in a pan over a low heat for 4–5 minutes until the apple is golden and soft. Add the cinnamon and cook, stirring, for 1–2 minutes. Heat the remaining butter in a frying pan. Dip the slices of bread in the egg so that they are lightly coated, then fry for 2 minutes on each side until the egg is set and golden. Serve with the apples and drizzle with maple syrup, if using.

FINGER FOOD

*Don't get confused and think this is a
diet book. The Paleo lifestyle in no way
limits the amount of food you eat and
there is no need to feel hungry.
Make sure you have a constant supply of
these quick Paleo snacks
to keep your appetite in check.*

Buffalo Wings • Chia Seed Crackers
Spiced Nuts • Courgette Fritters • Chorizo Balls
Mixed Pickled Vegetables • Chilli Salt Squid
Fresh Oysters • Guacamole • Baba Ganoush

BUFFALO WINGS

Serves: 2

YOU NEED

400 g chicken wings • ½ tablespoon coconut oil •
125 ml BBQ Sauce (see page 20) • 1 tablespoon nutritional yeast flakes
1 teaspoon allspice • 1 teaspoon smoked paprika

45 minutes

High in protein, B vitamins, phosphorous, calcium and zinc to
help strengthen bones and teeth.

B *Controls blood pressure*   **M** *Builds muscle*   **H** *Heart support*

Preheat the oven to 200°C/400°F/Gas 6. Cut each chicken wing into 3, discarding
the spiky wing tip. Place the coconut oil and wings into a roasting dish and shake to
coat the wings with oil. Roast for 30–40 minutes until the chicken is golden brown
and the skin is starting to crisp. Combine the sauce with the spices
and nutritional yeast. Remove the wings from the oven and toss through
the sauce mixture until coated. Serve immediately.

CHIA SEED CRACKERS

Makes: about 20 crackers

YOU NEED

65 g sesame seeds • 65 g chia seeds • 60 g pumpkin seeds

50 g LSA (ground linseed, sunflower seeds and almonds)

3 teaspoons seaweed flakes • 1 tablespoon nutritional yeast flakes

2 teaspoons tamari (wheat-free soy sauce)

*1 hour
10 minutes*

A good source of iodine and fibre and contains anti-inflammatory properties.

(T) *Regulates thyroid*   (G) *Gluten-free*   (C) *Lowers cholesterol*

Preheat the oven to 160°C/325°F/Gas 3. Line a baking tray with baking paper. Mix together the seeds, seaweed flakes and yeast flakes. Mix 225 ml of water with the tamari, then pour into the seed mixture and stir well. Rest for 5–10 minutes. Stir again and spread out over a baking tray. Press down with the back of a spoon and smooth out until 5 mm thick. Bake for 30 minutes. Cut into even cracker shapes, turn crackers over and bake for 20–25 minutes until crisp. Cool.
Store in an airtight container for 7–10 days.

SPICED NUTS

Serves: 2 / Makes 300 g

YOU NEED

2 tablespoons coconut oil • 100 g activated almonds (see page 9)

100 g activated cashew nuts • 100 g activated macadamia nuts

½ tablespoon dried garlic granules • 1 teaspoon chilli flakes

1 teaspoon sweet paprika • ½ tablespoon sea salt flakes

Nuts are packed with protein, essential fats, vitamin E and zinc to help keep the skin healthy, soft and supple.

B *Brain support*   **A** *Anti-inflammatory*   **H** *Heart support*

Preheat the oven to 200°C/400°F/Gas 6. Heat the oil in a roasting dish in the oven for 1–2 minutes. Add the nuts and toss to coat them in the oil. Roast for 10–12 minutes, tossing once. Meanwhile, combine the garlic, chilli, paprika and sea salt. Remove the nuts from the oven and toss the spice mix through them. Cool, then serve or store in an airtight container for a week.

COURGETTE FRITTERS

Makes: 8–10

YOU NEED

2 medium courgettes, grated • 1 organic egg, lightly beaten

2 spring onions, thinly sliced • 2 tablespoons coconut flour

2 tablespoons tapioca flour • 15 g coriander sprigs, chopped

1 teaspoon salt • 1 tablespoon coconut oil

Courgettes are full of fibre to help promote good bowel function and antioxidants to reduce the risk of strokes.

C *Lowers cholesterol*   **D** *Aids digestion*   **H** *Heart support*

Combine all of the ingredients, except the oil, in a bowl and stir well. Heat the oil in a frying pan over a medium heat. Use a large spoon to drop 3 heaped tablespoons of the mixture into pan and cook for 2–3 minutes on each side until golden. Rest the cooked fritters on kitchen paper and repeat with the remaining batter. Serve warm.

CHORIZO BALLS

Makes: about 16 balls

YOU NEED
4 tablespoons refined coconut oil • ½ onion, finely diced
3 garlic cloves, finely diced • ½ red pepper, finely diced
4 teaspoons smoked paprika • 1 tablespoon red wine vinegar • pinch of salt
350 g grass-fed pork mince • 1 handful of chopped flat-leaf parsley
lemon wedges

68

Chorizo is high in protein, so helps to boost the immune system.

E *Energy-boosting* **M** *Builds memory* **G** *Gluten-free*

Heat half the oil in a pan over a medium heat. Sauté the onions, garlic and red pepper for 4–5 minutes. Add the paprika, vinegar and salt and stir. Put in a bowl, add the mince and stir well. Cover and chill for 2 hours, or overnight. Roll a heaped tablespoon of the mixture to form a ball. Continue with the remaining mixture until you have made around 16 balls. In a frying pan, heat the remaining oil over a medium heat and cook 4–5 balls at a time for 7–8 minutes until browned and cooked through. Garnish with parsley and lemon.

MIXED PICKLED VEGETABLES

Makes: 1 × 1 litre jar

YOU NEED

2 carrots, diagonally sliced • ½ cauliflower, cut into small florets

1 bunch of breakfast radishes, quartered • ½ red pepper, sliced

2 jalapeño chillies, deseeded and quartered • 3 garlic cloves, squashed

1 bay leaf • ½ teaspoon whole black peppercorns • 3 tablespoons sea salt flakes

Promotes gut health as it contains healthy bacteria and helps in supplying essential vitamins and minerals including vitamins A, C and K, as well as iron and potassium.

D *Aids digestion*   **G** *Gluten-free*   **W** *Weight loss*

Fill a clean 1-litre jar with the vegetables, chillies, garlic, peppercorns and bay leaf. In a bowl, mix the salt into 875 ml of filtered water. Pour into the jar to cover the vegetables. Add more water if necessary. Make sure the jar is tightly sealed and leave to stand at room temperature for 2–5 days. Once a day, open the jar to release the gas and to taste the pickles. Scrape away any material that has risen to the top, then cover. When you are happy with the taste, chill. Store for up to 6–8 weeks.

CHILLI SALT SQUID

Serves: 4

YOU NEED

1 heaped teaspoon chilli flakes • 55 g activated cashew nuts (see page 9)

40 g coconut flour • 1 teaspoon salt • 30 g lard

400 g cleaned squid tubes • 2 organic eggs, beaten • lemon slices

Squid is high in protein and promotes good bone and teeth health.

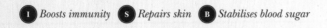

I *Boosts immunity*   **S** *Repairs skin*   **B** *Stabilises blood sugar*

Blitz the chilli, cashew nuts, flour and salt in a food processor until the mixture has a fine, breadcrumb-like texture. Spread on a plate. Split the squid lengthways down the middle, then into 4 cm lengths. Heat the lard in a wok. Dip 1 piece of squid at a time in the beaten egg then in the crumb mixture so that it is lightly coated. Fry for 2 minutes until golden brown. Drain on kitchen paper. Garnish with lemon.

FRESH OYSTERS

Serves: 4

YOU NEED
1 shallot, finely diced • 2 tablespoons red wine vinegar • ½ cucumber, finely diced
juice of 1 lime • salt • 8–12 large fresh oysters, cleaned and opened

Oysters are packed with zinc and some consider them to be powerful aphrodisiacs.

I *Boosts immunity*   **H** *Heart support*   **M** *Boosts metabolism*

In a bowl, mix the shallot and vinegar together. In another bowl, mix the cucumber, lime juice and a sprinkle of salt. Place the oysters on a platter (with ice if you want to keep them cold). Drizzle 1 teaspoon of vinegar sauce over half of the oysters, and 1 teaspoon of cucumber lime over the remaining oysters.

GUACAMOLE

Serves: 4

YOU NEED

2 ripe avocados, peeled and pitted • 25 g coriander leaves, finely chopped

2 shallots, finely diced • 2 red chillies, finely diced • juice of 1½ limes

Avocados are packed with heart-healthy fats to help keep the cardiovascular system healthy as well as improve the skin to keep it soft and wrinkle-free.

A *Anti-inflammatory*   I *Fights infection*   B *Blood pressure support*

Mash the avocadoes in a bowl. Add the remaining ingredients and mix well to combine. Serve immediately.

BABA GANOUSH

Serves: 4

YOU NEED

1 large aubergine • juice of 1 lemon • 3 tablespoons tahini
2 garlic cloves, finely diced • 10 g flat-leaf parsley, finely chopped
1 tablespoon macadamia or olive oil • ½ teaspoon smoked paprika • salt

High in fibre, B vitamins, potassium and magnesium
and can help with weight management.

A *Anti-inflammatory* **A** *Anti-ageing* **C** *Cholesterol lowering*

Preheat the oven to 180°C/350°F/Gas 4. Prick the aubergine a few times with a fork
and char on the flame of the hob for a few minutes on each side until the skin
is blistering and softened. Put into a roasting dish and bake for 15–20 minutes
until soft. Cool slightly and remove the skin. Blitz the aubergine flesh with the
remaining ingredients and seasoning in a food processor until the desired
consistency is reached. Serve immediately.

SIDES & SALADS

*These sides and salads can easily make
a meal on their own but pair one or two
dishes with some eggs, seafood or a quick
seared steak and you have a simple
and delicious feast.*

Honey-Roasted Baby Carrots • Spring Onion
Carrot Noodles • Green Salad with Tahini
Dressing • Pumpkin with Cashew Cheese
Brussels Sprouts with Bacon • Roasted Beetroot
& Rocket Salad • Asian-Style Duck Salad
Sweet Potato & Sumac Fries • Whole Roasted
Mushrooms • Chicken Coleslaw • Chinese
Broccoli with Almonds • Sashimi Salad

HONEY-ROASTED BABY CARROTS

Serves: 2

YOU NEED

1 tablespoon coconut or olive oil • 2 tablespoons honey
20 g flat-leaf parsley, finely chopped • 1 bunch of mixed baby carrots, peeled

Carrots are rich in vitamin A, which is good for vision, and also contain vitamin C to help boost the immune system.

D *Aids digestion*   **H** *Heart support*   **C** *Lowers cholesterol*

Preheat the oven to 180°C/350°F/Gas 4. In a pan, mix the oil, honey and 15 g of the parsley and heat until combined. Arrange the carrots in a single layer in roasting dish. Pour the honey mix over and toss to coat the carrots evenly. Roast for 40 minutes, tossing once or twice. Top with the remaining parsley to serve.

SPRING ONION CARROT NOODLES

Serves: 2

YOU NEED

3 large carrots, peeled • 1 tablespoon sesame oil

1 tablespoon grated ginger • 2 spring onions, thinly sliced

1 teaspoon chilli flakes • 2 teaspoons honey

1 small bunch of coriander • 1 tablespoon toasted sesame seeds

Carrots are high in fibre to aid good digestive health while spring onions contain sulphur to help control blood pressure.

C *Lowers cholesterol* **A** *Antibacterial* **H** *Heart support*

Use a vegetable peeler or spiralizer to slice the carrots into thin noodles. Heat the sesame oil in a wok. Add the ginger, spring onions and chilli flakes and sauté for 1 minute. Add the carrots. Top with the honey and cook, stirring, for 4 minutes. The carrots should still have a bite. Top with the coriander and sesame seeds and serve.

GREEN SALAD WITH TAHINI DRESSING

Serves: 1 as a main or 2–4 as a side

YOU NEED

100 g mixed lettuce leaves • ½ avocado, peeled, pitted and sliced

½ medium cucumber, sliced • 1 handful of sugar snap peas, podded

1 handful of pea shoots • 2 mint leaves, roughly chopped

3 tablespoons Creamy Tahini Dressing (see page 18) • 30 g pumpkin seeds, roasted

High in minerals to support the cardiovascular
system and respiratory health.

 B *Strengthens bones*   E *Eye protection*   H *Heart support*

Combine all of the green ingredients in a bowl. Pour over the dressing and toss.
Top with pumpkin seeds and serve.

87

PUMPKIN WITH CASHEW CHEESE

Serves: 4

YOU NEED

2 teaspoons sea salt • 1 teaspoon chilli flakes

1 rosemary sprig, leaves removed and chopped

¼ pumpkin (can use any variety), cored and sliced • 1 tablespoon coconut oil

2–3 tablespoons Cashew Cheese (see page 30)

Pumpkins are high in fibre and low in calories to help with weight management, and also contain vitamin A to help with vision.

S *Repairs skin*   **H** *Heart support*   **C** *Lowers cholesterol*

Preheat oven to 200°C/400°F/Gas 6. Mix the salt, chilli and rosemary together. Rub the pumpkin in the oil and sprinkle with the salt mix. Roast in the oven for 15 minutes. Check and turn if needed, then roast for another 10 minutes until the pumpkin is soft and browned. Crumble the cashew cheese over the pumpkin and serve.

BRUSSELS SPROUTS WITH BACON

Serves: 4

YOU NEED
2 good handfuls of Brussels sprouts • 20 g activated pecans (see page 9)
1 rasher grass-fed bacon, diced • ½ tablespoon olive oil (optional)

Bacon and Brussels sprouts are packed with iron to help with the formation of red blood cells.

Ⓔ *Energy-boosting*　Ⓘ *Boosts immunity*　Ⓐ *Anti-inflammatory*

Steam the Brussels sprouts over hot water for 4–5 minutes until just softening. Set aside. Toast the pecans in a dry frying pan for 4–5 minutes. Set aside. Cook the bacon until browned and crisp, then add the Brussels sprouts and pecans and toss together. Drizzle with olive oil, if needed, and serve.

ROASTED BEETROOT & ROCKET SALAD

Serves: 1

YOU NEED

1 large beetroot, cut into eighths • 1 tablespoon coconut oil

2 tablespoons toasted sunflower seeds • 1 large handful of rocket

1 large handful of spinach • 2 tablespoons Cashew Cheese (see page 30)

2 tablespoons Simple Salad Vinaigrette (see page 16)

salt and freshly ground black pepper

Beetroot is high in nitrates, which helps blood vessels to relax, while rocket has high levels of chlorophyll.

A *Anti-inflammatory* **D** *Detoxifying* **C** *Lowers cholesterol*

Preheat oven to 200°C/400°F/Gas 6. Toss the beetroot in oil and season. Place in a baking dish and roast for 20–30 minutes until the beetroot feels soft when pricked with a fork. In the last 5 minutes of roasting, add the sunflower seeds.
In a bowl, mix the remaining ingredients. Add the beetroot and sunflower seeds and toss together to combine.

ASIAN-STYLE DUCK SALAD

Serves: 1

YOU NEED

1 organic duck breast with skin on • 1 teaspoon salt

1 teaspoon Chinese five-spice powder • 1 carrot, julienned

1 baby bok choy, roughly chopped • 40 g beansprouts

20 g mint and/or coriander leaves • ½ tablespoon sesame oil

1 teaspoon maple syrup • ½ tablespoon fish sauce • juice of 1 lime

Duck is a good source of protein and is rich in vitamins and minerals, particularly selenium to boost the immune system, while bok choy is full of vitamins A, C and K.

S *Skin & hair support* **I** *Fights infection* **B** *Strengthens bones*

Preheat the oven to 180°C/350°F/Gas 4. Combine the salt and five-spice powder and rub over the duck skin. Heat the oil in a pan over a high heat. Cook the duck, skin side down, for 6–7 minutes until browned and crispy. Transfer to a baking tray, skin side up, and cook in the oven for 10 minutes. Rest for 5 minutes. Combine the vegetables and herbs. Slice the duck and add to the vegetables. Whisk the maple syrup, lime juice and fish sauce together. Pour over the salad and toss to combine.

SWEET POTATO & SUMAC FRIES

Serves: 2

YOU NEED

400–500 g sweet potatoes, cut into chips • 1 tablespoon ghee or duck fat

2 teaspoons sumac • salt

Sweet potatoes are rich in beta-carotene, which helps to reduce the risk of heart disease and to fight off infections.

E *Eye protection*   **A** *Anti-inflammatory*   **B** *Regulates blood sugar*

Preheat the oven to 200°C/400°F/Gas 6. Toss the sweet potatoes in the ghee or duck fat, then arrange on a baking tray, spaced apart. Sprinkle with sumac and salt and roast for about 30–40 minutes until soft in the centre and golden brown. Turn halfway through roasting so the potatoes are evenly cooked. Serve hot.

WHOLE ROASTED MUSHROOMS

Serves: 2–4

YOU NEED

5–6 Portobello mushrooms • 1 tablespoon olive oil

4 tablespoons Chilli Sambal (see page 24) • 2 rosemary sprigs, leaves removed • salt

Mushrooms contain vitamin D, calcium, potassium and are a good source of B vitamins to help strengthen the immune system and also promote weight loss.

A *Anti-inflammatory*   **H** *Heart support*   **B** *Strengthens bones*

Toss the mushrooms with half the oil, chilli sambal, rosemary and a sprinkle of salt. Ensure that the chilli is rubbed over the mushrooms. Cover and marinate for 1–4 hours. Preheat the oven to 180°C/350°F/Gas 4. Pour the remaining oil into a roasting dish. Spread out the mushrooms, gill side up, leaving space between them, and cook for 35–40 minutes until the mushrooms are soft and juicy.

CHICKEN COLESLAW

Serves: 1

YOU NEED

2 tablespoons Paleo Mayo (see page 28) • juice of ½ lemon • salt

1 free-range chicken breast, cooked and shredded • 150 g red cabbage, shredded

½ small fennel, finely sliced • 1 apple, peeled, cored and julienned

5 g mint, finely shredded

Packed with fibre and lots of essential vitamins and minerals including
vitamins A, B, C and K

I *Boosts immunity*   **E** *Eye protection*   **H** *Heart support*

In a bowl, whisk the mayo and lemon juice together, adding 1–2 tablespoons water,
if needed. Season with a pinch of salt. Combine the remaining ingredients in
another bowl. Pour the dressing over and toss to mix well.

CHINESE BROCCOLI WITH ALMONDS

Serves: 2–4

YOU NEED

80 g activated almonds (see page 9) • 2 teaspoons sesame oil

5 g piece ginger, peeled and freshly grated

1 bunch of Chinese broccoli, chopped into 5 cm pieces

1 tablespoon tamari (wheat-free soy sauce) • 1 teaspoon chilli flakes

10 minutes

Promotes heart health, helps to lower cholesterol and keeps the skin healthy.

I *Boosts immunity*   **E** *Energy-boosting*   **B** *Strengthens bones*

Toast the almonds in a dry frying pan over a medium heat. Set aside. Heat the oil
and ginger in a pan, then add the broccoli. Toss to coat in the oil, then pour over
the tamari and chilli flakes. Keep stirring until the broccoli is well coated. Add
1 tablespoon of water, cover and steam for 1–2 minutes until cooked. Uncover,
sprinkle with almonds and chilli, stir and cook for 1–2 minutes. Serve hot.

SASHIMI SALAD

Serves: 1

YOU NEED

2 tablespoons tamari (wheat-free soy sauce) • juice of 1 lemon
sprinkle of dulse (seaweed flakes) • 1 handful of frisee lettuce
1 handful of watercress • 200 g fresh sushi-grade tuna, sliced
3 good-sized radishes, shaved • 2 teaspoons black sesame seeds

Watercress is a rich source of vitamin K, calcium and manganese to keep teeth strong, while tuna contains plenty of healthy omega-3 fats.

I *Boosts immunity* **H** *Heart support* **B** *Strengthens bones*

Whisk the tamari, lemon juice and dulse together in a bowl. Set aside. Arrange the lettuce and watercress on a plate, top with the tuna slices and sprinkle with the radishes and sesame seeds. Pour over the dressing and serve.

MAINS

All of these recipes can be doubled or tripled to make larger quantities if necessary. I suggest always having extra cooked meats on hand for snacks or to add fresh or cooked vegetables for a new dish altogether.

Scallops with Parsnip Purée
Whole Baked Snapper • Beef Bourguignon
Poule au Pot • Pot au Feu • Caveman Burger
Garlic & Chilli Prawns • Rib-Eye Steaks with Minty
Peas • Cauliflower Fried Rice • Pork & Pears
Bangers & Sweet Potato Mash • Mediterranean
Lamb • Courgette Bolognese • Paleo Lasagne
Seafood Chowder • Vegetable Curry
Mushroom & Leek Soup • Butternut Squash
Gnocchi • Wild Fish with Salsa Verde

SCALLOPS WITH PARSNIP PURÉE

Serves: 2

YOU NEED

2 tablespoons coconut oil • 1 shallot, diced • 2 small parsnips, roughly chopped
375 ml Chicken Stock (see page 14) • 1 tablespoon butter (optional)
4 large fresh sea scallops • 1 small handful of pea shoots • salt • juice of 1 lemon

Full of protein, B vitamins, vitamin C and potassium to keep the heart healthy.

I *Immunity support* **M** *Enhances memory* **B** *Strengthens bones*

Heat 1 tablespoon of the oil in a lidded pan. Brown the shallot and parsnips. Season and add the stock. Cover and cook for 30 minutes until the parsnips are soft. Strain, reserving the liquid. Blend the parsnips and onions in a food processor, adding some reserved liquid until smooth, then strain. Heat the remaining oil and butter, if using, in pan until bubbling. Add the scallops, season and cook for 3 minutes on each side. Serve over the purée with the pea shoots and lemon juice.

WHOLE BAKED SNAPPER

Serves: 1–2

YOU NEED

1 whole snapper, cleaned and gutted • 2 lemons, 1 sliced, the other juiced

30 g flat-leaf parsley • 10 g thyme, leaves picked • 1 tablespoon coconut oil

salt • 20 g organic butter • 2 shallots, finely diced

1 large leek, thinly sliced in half rounds

Rich in omega-3 fatty acids and selenium to help improve brain function.

I *Boosts immunity* **E** *Eye protection* **H** *Heart support*

Preheat the oven to 180°C/350°F/Gas 4. Stuff the snapper with lemon slices, parsley and thyme. Rub both sides of the fish with half the oil and salt. Heat the remaining oil in a pan over a medium to high heat. Cook the fish for 2 minutes on each side. Put in a roasting dish and bake for 10 minutes. Heat the butter in the same pan. Add the shallots and leeks and cook for 6–8 minutes until the leeks are soft. Add the lemon juice and cook for 5 minutes. Serve fish on top of leeks.

BEEF BOURGUIGNON

Serves: 4

YOU NEED

800 g grass-fed chuck steak, cut into large cubes • 2 tablespoons flour

3 tablespoons tapioca flour • 2 tablespoons coconut oil

1 tablespoon red wine vinegar • 2 celery sticks, diced • 2 leeks, finely sliced

400 g can chopped tomatoes • 500 ml Chicken Stock (see page 14) • 2 bay leaves

1 quantity Cauliflower White Sauce (see page 34)

salt and freshly ground black pepper

2 hours
30 minutes

High in iron, omega-3 fatty acids, B vitamins, zinc and potassium to help strengthen the immune system.

B *Strengthens bones*　**A** *Anti-inflammatory*　**E** *Eye protection*

Dust the steak in the flour. Heat half the oil in a casserole dish and brown the meat all over, adding half the vinegar. Set aside. Add more oil if needed and sauté the celery and leeks in the casserole dish for 6–8 minutes until starting to soften. Add the tomatoes and stock, then bring to the boil. Remove from the heat and blend with a hand-held blender until smooth. Return the meat to the casserole dish with the remaining vinegar and bay leaves and simmer, covered, for 1–2 hours until the meat is tender. Serve with the white sauce and season.

113

POULE AU POT

Serves: 4

YOU NEED

1 whole free-range chicken • 1 lemon, sliced • ½ bulb garlic, cut in half

4 thyme sprigs • 1 small handful of flat-leaf parsley

2 litres Chicken Stock (see page 14) or water • 5 baby spring onions, trimmed

2 carrots, chopped into batons • salt and freshly ground black pepper

Full of vitamin D to help strengthen bones and teeth and vitamin B
to boost the immune system.

H *Heart support*   **I** *Fights infection*   **E** *Eye protection*

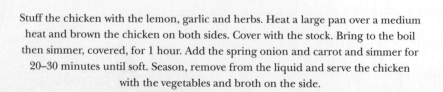

Stuff the chicken with the lemon, garlic and herbs. Heat a large pan over a medium
heat and brown the chicken on both sides. Cover with the stock. Bring to the boil
then simmer, covered, for 1 hour. Add the spring onion and carrot and simmer for
20–30 minutes until soft. Season, remove from the liquid and serve the chicken
with the vegetables and broth on the side.

POT AU FEU

Serves: 4

YOU NEED

4 grass-fed beef shanks • 1 kg grass-fed beef brisket

salt and freshly ground black pepper • 3 bay leaves • stalks of 1 bunch of parsley

1 onion, sliced • 1 bunch of baby carrots, peeled

2 turnips, peeled and quartered • 3 celery sticks, cut into 10 cm pieces

Health-restoring, boosts joint function and helps to strengthen bones.

I *Boosts immunity* A *Anti-inflammatory* M *Boosts memory*

Put the beef shanks and brisket into a casserole dish and season well. Add the bay
leaves and parsley stalks. Pour in 2.5 litres of water and cover with a lid. Bring to
the boil, then simmer for 2 hours, skimming off any foam. Remove the bay leaves
and parsley and add the remaining ingredients. Simmer until the vegetables have
softened. Serve the broth, meat and vegetables with condiments of your choice.

CAVEMAN BURGER

Serves: 2

YOU NEED

15 g flat-leaf parsley • 1 small onion, cut into rings • 2 garlic cloves

salt • 300 g grass-fed beef mince • 1 organic egg yolk

1 tablespoon coconut oil • 2–4 outside leaves of iceberg lettuce

½ avocado, peeled, pitted and sliced • 1 tablespoon Paleo Tomato Sauce

(see page 26) • 1 tablespoon Paleo Mayo (see page 28)

35 minutes

This burger has a low glycaemic index (GI) and is high
in protein, potassium, iron and zinc.

B *Strengthens bones*   **E** *Energising*   **I** *Boosts immunity*

Preheat the oven to 180°C/350°F/Gas 4. Pulse the parsley, half the onions and
the garlic in a food processor until finely chopped. Season the mince and add the
parsley mix and egg yolk. Bring together, divide in half and shape into 2 patties.
Heat the oil in a pan. Cook the patties for a few minutes on each side to brown.
Place on a baking tray and bake for 10–15 minutes. In the same pan, cook the
remaining onions until soft. Serve the patties wrapped in lettuce with the onions,
avocado and condiments.

119

GARLIC & CHILLI PRAWNS

Serves: 2

YOU NEED
3–4 tablespoons Chilli Sambal (see page 24)

300 g raw prawns, peeled and deveined • 2 tablespoons sesame oil

1 bunch of broccolini or tenderstem broccoli • ½ lemon, plus extra to garnish

1 tablespoon sesame seeds

Prawns are an excellent source of protein, vitamin D, selenium, copper and zinc and can help boost the immune system.

B *Strengthens bones*   **A** *Anti-ageing*   **M** *Boosts memory*

Stir the chilli sambal through the prawns. Cover and chill for 1–2 hours. Heat a wok with half the sesame oil over a medium heat. Add the prawns and stir over the heat for 4–5 minutes. Set aside. Add the remaining oil to the wok and cook the broccolini for 4–5 minutes. Return the prawns to the wok and heat for 1–2 minutes. Squeeze the lemon over the prawns, sprinkle with sesame seeds and serve with the juices from the wok and lemon wedges.

RIB-EYE STEAKS WITH MINTY PEAS

Serves: 2

YOU NEED

salt and freshly ground black pepper • 2 grass-fed rib-eye steaks
100 ml Chicken Stock (see page 14) • 100 g frozen peas
1 handful of mint leaves, finely chopped • 10 g organic butter

Rich in omega fatty acids, protein and vitamin B12 to help in the
formation of healthy red blood cells.

I *Boosts immunity*　**H** *Heart support*　**M** *Boosts memory*

Season the steaks. Heat a frying pan over a high heat. Fry each steak for 5–6 minutes
on either side or to own preference. Heat the stock in a pan, add the peas and cook
for 2–3 minutes. Drain, add the mint and butter and stir well.
Rest the steaks for 4–5 minutes. Serve with the peas.

CAULIFLOWER FRIED RICE

Serves: 2

YOU NEED

1 medium cauliflower, broken into florets • 2 teaspoons sesame oil
1 small onion, diced • 1 rasher of grass-fed bacon, diced • 10 prawns
2 organic eggs, lightly beaten • 80 g peas, fresh or frozen
2 tablespoons tamari (wheat-free soy sauce)
1 tablespoon Paleo Tomato Sauce (see page 26)

20 minutes

Peas contain fibre so balance blood sugar levels while cauliflower and bacon contain choline to help boost memory and keep the brain healthy.

A *Anti-inflammatory* **E** *Energising* **I** *Boosts immunity*

Blitz the cauliflower in a food processor until it resembles breadcrumbs. Heat the oil in a wok over a medium to high heat. Sauté the onion until soft. Add the bacon and cook until it begins to brown and crisp. Add the prawns and sauté for 2 minutes. Add the cauliflower to the wok and stir. Working quickly, make a well in the centre and pour in the egg, stirring through the cauliflower. Mix in the peas, tamari and tomato sauce.

PORK & PEARS

Serves: 2

YOU NEED
salt • 400 g grass-fed pork belly, scored, rinsed and patted dry • 2 pears
juice of ¼ pineapple • olive oil, for drizzling • 1 flat-leaf parsley sprig

Grass-fed pork is full of protein, B vitamins and zinc to boost the immune system while pears are full of fibre to help control blood sugar levels.

B *Strengthens bones* **E** *Energising* **H** *Heart support*

Sprinkle the salt over the pork. Cover with kitchen paper and chill for 1 hour. Preheat the oven to 220°C/425°F/Gas 7. Juice 1 of the pears. Peel and quarter the remaining pear. Drizzle the oil into a roasting dish and place the quartered pears in the base. Place the pork on top. Roast for 20–25 minutes until the skin starts to crackle. Remove the pork from the oven and reduce the temperature to 160°C/325°F/Gas 3. Pour the pear and pineapple juice around the pork. Roast for 1–1½ hours. Slice the pork, garnish with the parsley and serve with the pears.

BANGERS & SWEET POTATO MASH

Serves: 1

YOU NEED

1 sweet potato, peeled and diced • 2 good-quality grass-fed pork sausages
3 garlic cloves, unpeeled • 2 rosemary sprigs • 1 tablespoon olive oil • salt
1 tablespoon butter • 1 tablespoon Paleo Onion Jam (see page 32) (optional)

Rich in vitamins and minerals and can help to stabilise blood sugar levels.

A *Anti-inflammatory*   **E** *Energising*   **H** *Heart support*

Preheat the oven to 180°C/350°F/Gas 4. Place the sweet potato, sausages, garlic and rosemary in a roasting dish. Drizzle with the oil and season. Roast for 15 minutes. Turn the sausages and cook for 15 minutes until the potatoes are soft and the sausages are cooked. Discard the rosemary. Place the sweet potato in a bowl, squeeze in the roasted garlic, add the butter and mash. Place the sausages on top of the mash and top with onion jam, if using.

MEDITERRANEAN LAMB

Serves: 4

YOU NEED
1 kg piece of boned, grass-fed lamb (leg or shoulder), cut into rough cubes

1 aubergine, sliced into wedges • 1 red pepper, sliced

10 g flat-leaf parsley, roughly chopped • 2 tablespoons olive oil • 1 teaspoon salt

1 tablespoon cumin seeds • 6 Roma tomatoes, sliced into rounds • juice of 1 lemon

Low in calories, high in protein and iron from the lamb and packed with antioxidants from the tomatoes and red peppers.

 Strengthens hair   *Heart support*   *Repairs muscle*

Preheat the oven to 160°C/325°F/Gas 3. Place the lamb, aubergine, red pepper and parsley in a baking dish. Drizzle with the oil and sprinkle with salt and cumin. Toss to combine. Top with the tomato slices and squeeze over the lemon juice. Pour in 125 ml of water, cover with foil and bake for 1½ hours. Uncover, increase the temperature to 190°C/375°F/Gas 5 and cook for 20–25 minutes until slightly reduced and browned on top.

COURGETTE BOLOGNESE

Serves: 2

YOU NEED

60 ml olive oil • 80 g shallots, diced • 30 g diced garlic

40 ml red wine vinegar • 600 g grass-fed beef mince • salt • 140 g tomato purée

400 g can chopped tomatoes • 2 medium courgettes

chopped parsley, to garnish

Courgettes are high in fibre to aid digestion, stabilise blood sugar levels and prevent constipation while grass-fed beef contains lots of iron.

I *Boosts immunity* **E** *Energising* **A** *Anti–inflammatory*

Heat 2 tablespoons of the oil in a pan over a medium heat. Sauté the shallots and garlic until softened. Add the vinegar and mince. Season and cook for 6–8 minutes until browned. Add the remaining oil, salt and the tomato purée and stir until the mince is coated. Add the tomatoes and 125 ml of water. Bring to the boil. Simmer for 30 minutes until thick. Use a grater or spiralizer to make noodles from the courgettes. Serve the Bolognese over the noodles and garnish with parsley.

PALEO LASAGNE

Serves: 4–6

YOU NEED

2 aubergines, sliced • 30 g salt • coconut oil

1 quantity Cauliflower White Sauce Sauce (see page 34)

1 quantity Bolognese Mince (see page 132)

High in fibre, protein, B vitamins and magnesium to help with fatigue.

H *Heart support* **E** *Energising* **I** *Boosts immunity*

Spread the aubergine out on kitchen paper. Sprinkle with the salt. Leave for 30 minutes. Preheat the oven to 200°C/400°F/Gas 6. Oil the baking dish. Put a layer of aubergine in the base of the dish, followed by a thin layer of white sauce. Top with a thick layer of mince and continue to layer with the remaining ingredients, finishing with white sauce. Bake for 30–40 minutes until golden brown and serve hot.

SEAFOOD CHOWDER

Serves: 2

YOU NEED

3 tablespoons olive oil • 1 onion, chopped • 200 g chopped leeks

200 g chopped cauliflower • 150 g chopped parsnip

500 ml Chicken Stock (see page 14) • 1 small bunch of dill

400 g mixed fish and seafood

fresh lemon, to taste • a pinch of sea salt

Seafood is packed with essential vitamins and minerals including omega-3 fatty acids to boost energy and help keep the heart healthy.

B *Brain support* **A** *Anti-inflammatory* **E** *Eye protection*

Heat 2 tablespoons of the oil in a lidded pan over a medium heat. Sauté the onion and other vegetables with salt. Add the stock and most of the dill, cover and bring to the boil. Simmer for 30 minutes. Remove the dill and strain the vegetables, reserving the liquid. Blitz the vegetables in a food processor, adding some reserved liquid until smooth. Fry the fish and seafood mix until just coloured. Pour the purée over the seafood and simmer for 4–5 minutes until the seafood is cooked. Garnish with the remaining dill and lemon juice and serve.

VEGETABLE CURRY

Serves: 2

YOU NEED

2 tablespoons coconut oil • 2–3 tablespoons green curry paste, depending on taste
1 small onion, sliced • ¼ cauliflower, cut into florets • 400 g can coconut milk
3 ripe tomatoes, diced • 80 g mangetout, trimmed and cut in half
2 teaspoons fish sauce • juice of ½ lime • coriander leaves, to garnish

25 minutes

Lactose-free, loaded with fibre, vitamins and minerals including vitamins A, B, C and K to help boost the immune system.

A *Anti-inflammatory*   **D** *Aids digestion*   **E** *Energising*

Heat the oil in a wok over a medium heat, add the curry paste and onion and cook for 4–5 minutes until the onion is soft and the paste is fragrant. Add the cauliflower and sauté for 1 minute. Pour in the coconut milk and add the tomatoes. Simmer for 7–8 minutes. Add the mangetout and fish sauce and mix. Remove from the heat, squeeze over the lime juice, garnish with coriander and serve.

MUSHROOM & LEEK SOUP

Serves: 2

YOU NEED

1 tablespoon coconut or olive oil • 1 rosemary sprig

150 g button mushrooms, sliced • 1 medium leek, roughly chopped

80 g cauliflower, chopped • ½ onion, diced

2 garlic cloves • 400 ml Chicken Stock (see page 14)

Leeks can help to support the cardiovascular system while mushrooms are
packed with calcium and potassium to help strengthen bones.

I *Boosts immunity* **E** *Energising* **C** *Lowers cholesterol*

Heat the oil in a lidded pan over a medium heat. Add the rosemary and vegetables
and cook for 5 minutes until browned. Season and add the stock. Cook, covered, for
1 hour, stirring occasionally until the vegetables are soft. Leave to cool. Remove the
rosemary. Blend with a hand-held blender, adding more stock if needed. Serve hot.

BUTTERNUT SQUASH GNOCCHI

Serves: 2

YOU NEED
coconut oil • 250 g butternut squash, peeled, deseeded and cubed
½ sweet potato (200 g), peeled and cubed • salt • 100 g coconut flour
200 g tapioca flour • 1 organic egg, slightly beaten
1 tablespoon butter • 100 g mushrooms, sliced • 30 g baby spinach

Low in calories, full of fibre and packed with potassium to help
lower blood pressure and reduce the risk of strokes.

B *Strengthens bones*   **A** *Anti-inflammatory*   **H** *Heart support*

Preheat the oven to 180°C/350°F/Gas 4. Oil a roasting dish with the coconut oil.
Put the butternut squash and sweet potato into the dish. Season with salt and roast
for 20–25 minutes until soft. Cool. Blitz the vegetables, coconut flour, half of the
tapioca flour and the egg in a food processor until smooth. Spread the remaining
tapioca flour over a clean, flat surface. Break the dough into small pieces and roll
into 3 cm tubes. Cut into smaller pieces. Cook the gnocchi in boiling water for
2–3 minutes until they float to the top. Drain. Heat the butter in a pan. Cook the
mushrooms and spinach for 5 minutes until soft. Mix in the gnocchi and serve.

WILD FISH WITH SALSA VERDE

Serves: 2

YOU NEED

2 tablespoons coconut oil • salt and freshly ground black pepper

2 × 160 g wild white fish fillets (bream, snapper), skin left on

1 small handful of basil leaves • 1 small handful of mint leaves

2 anchovies in olive oil • 1 garlic clove • 20 g activated macadamia nuts (see page 9)

juice of 1 lemon • 60 g cherry tomatoes, quartered

Helps to lower blood pressure as fish is packed with healthy omega-3 fatty acids and tomatoes contain potassium.

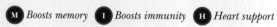
M *Boosts memory*   **I** *Boosts immunity*   **H** *Heart support*

Heat the oil in a pan over a medium to high heat. Season the fish on both sides and place in the pan, skin side down. Cook for 4–5 minutes until the skin is crispy and golden. Turn and cook for 4–5 minutes. Whizz the basil, mint, anchovies, garlic, macadamia nuts and lemon juice in a food processer until finely chopped. Mix with the tomatoes. Serve the salsa verde on top of the fish.

SWEETS

Strictly speaking you won't need to include these sweet treats into your Paleo lifestyle – eliminating sugar and processed foods will change the way you desire this kind of food. However, these recipes are Paleo-friendly and will be the perfect treat for visitors or to give you a little extra variety in your diet.

Nutty Raspberry Friand Bites
Paleo Chocolate Brownie • Nut Energy Bars
Salted Caramel Energy Balls
Roasted Peach Crumble

NUTTY RASPBERRY FRIAND BITES

Makes: 12 mini muffins

YOU NEED

75 g organic butter or coconut oil, melted, plus extra for greasing

30 g coconut flour • 75 g ground hazelnuts • 1 teaspoon baking powder

2 organic eggs, separated • 4 tablespoons maple syrup

50 g frozen or fresh raspberries

Contains lauric acid from the coconut flour to help boost the immune system and strengthen bones, while raspberries can help stabilise blood sugar levels.

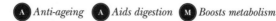

(A) *Anti-ageing* (A) *Aids digestion* (M) *Boosts metabolism*

Preheat the oven to 160°C/325°F/Gas 3. Use melted butter or oil to grease a 12-hole mini muffin tin. Combine the flour, hazelnuts and baking powder. Add the egg yolks and melted oil or butter and mix. Using an electric mixer, beat the egg whites to form soft peaks, then while the mixer is on, slowly pour in the maple syrup and beat until stiff. Fold the egg whites into the flour, one-third at a time. Place a heaped teaspoon of batter into each muffin hole. Bake for 15 minutes. Leave to cool. Once cool, decorate each friand bite with a raspberry.

PALEO CHOCOLATE BROWNIE

Makes: 16 squares

YOU NEED

60 ml coconut oil, plus extra for greasing

8 Medjool dates, pitted and roughly chopped • 80 ml maple syrup

70 g ground almonds • 2 tablespoons coconut flour • 1 teaspoon baking powder

45 g raw cacao powder • 1 courgette, grated • 4 organic eggs, lightly beaten

Cacao is good for the brain and may help to improve memory, while dates
are packed with minerals to help strengthen bones.

I *Immunity boosting* **E** *Energising* **H** *Heart support*

Preheat the oven to 200°C/400°F/Gas 6. Grease a 20 cm square tin. Mix the dates,
syrup and oil in a pan and heat gently for 3–5 minutes. Stir and break up the dates.
Combine the ground almonds, coconut flour, baking powder, cacao and courgette.
Add the eggs and the date mixture and stir until well combined. Pour into a tin
and bake for 20–25 minutes, or until set. Cool in the tin, then turn out
and cut into squares.

NUT ENERGY BARS

Makes: 10 bars

YOU NEED

75 g activated cashew nuts (see page 9) • 80 g activated almonds (see page 9)

100 g activated macadamia nuts (see page 9) • 25 g goji berries • 30 g chia seeds

30 g sesame seeds • ½ teaspoon sea salt • 125 ml honey

Nuts and seeds are high in fibre and are packed with healthy omega-3 fatty acids to help lower cholesterol.

B *Strengthens bones* **S** *Repairs skin* **H** *Heart support*

Preheat the oven to 180°C/350°F/Gas 4. Line a 20cm baking tin with baking paper. Pulse the nuts and goji berries in a food processor until finely chopped. Tip into a bowl and add the seeds and salt. Heat the honey gently to thin, then stir through the nut mixture. Pour into the tin and press down with the back of a spoon. Bake for 15–20 minutes. Cool for 30 minutes before removing from the tin. Once cooled completely, cut into bars.

SALTED CARAMEL ENERGY BALLS

Makes: 12–15 balls

YOU NEED

200 g desiccated coconut • 12 Medjool dates, pitted
1 teaspoon natural vanilla extract • 1 teaspoon sea salt flakes
2 tablespoons sesame seeds, for coating

Coconut and dates can help boost energy and stabilise blood sugar levels.

E *Energising* **A** *Anti-ageing* **M** *Boosts memory*

Blitz the coconut, dates, vanilla and salt in a food processor until chopped and well combined. Remove and roll into small balls, about 30 g each. Coat in sesame seeds and serve.

ROASTED PEACH CRUMBLE

Serves: 4

YOU NEED

40 g activated pecans (see page 9) • 2 tablespoons coconut flour
30 g desiccated coconut • 2 ripe peaches, halved • 1½ tablespoons sunflower seeds
40 g organic butter or coconut oil • 1 tablespoon maple syrup (optional)
½ teaspoon ground cinnamon

50 minutes

High in fibre to help the digestive system and prevent constipation.

A *Anti-ageing*   **S** *Skin repairing*   **E** *Eyesight support*

Preheat the oven to 200°C/400°C/Gas 6. Combine the pecans with the flour, coconut and pumpkin seeds. Roughly rub the butter into the flour mix with your fingertips. Chill. Place the peaches in a baking dish, sprinkle with the cinnamon and drizzle with maple syrup, if using. Roast for 20 minutes until softened. Spoon 2 tablespoons of the flour mix onto each peach half, then bake for 10 minutes until golden brown.

INDEX

Acknowledgements

We would like to thank everybody involved in the
conception and making of this book.

Elisa it was wonderful to have the opportunity to work with you
for the first time, thank you.

To Catie, Alice and Kathy, once again – a great team.

To Kath and Jodi, assistant extraordinaires, and to our family
for their continued support and help day to day.
x Amelia and Alex

Paleo by Amelia Wasiliev and Alex Wasiliev

First published in 2016 by Hachette Books
(Marabout)
This English hardback edition published in
2016 by Hardie Grant Books

Hardie Grant Books (UK)
52-54 Southwark Street
London SE1 1UN
hardiegrant.co.uk

Hardie Grant Books (Australia)
Ground Floor, Building 1
658 Church Street
Melbourne, VIC 3121
hardiegrant.com.au

The moral rights of Amelia Wasiliev and Alex
Wasiliev to be identified as the authors of this
work have been asserted by them in accordance
with the Copyright, Designs and Patents Act 1988.

Text © Amelia Wasiliev and Alex Wasiliev
Photography © Elisa Watson

All rights reserved. No part of this publication
may be reproduced, stored in a retrieval
system or transmitted in any form by any
means, electronic, electrostatic, magnetic
tape, mechanical, photocopying, recording or
otherwise, without the prior written permission
of the Publisher.

British Library Cataloguing-in-Publication
Data. A catalogue record for this book is
available from the British Library.

ISBN: 978-1-78488-070-5

Publisher: Catie Ziller
Authors: Amelia Wasiliev & Alex Wasiliev
Designer & illustrator: Alice Chadwick
Photographer: Elisa Watson
Food Stylist: Amelia Wasiliev
Editor: Kathy Steer

For the English hardback edition:
Publisher: Kate Pollard
Senior Editor: Kajal Mistry
Editorial Assistant: Hannah Roberts
Cover Design: Hardie Grant Books
Colour Reproduction by p2d

Printed and bound in China by 1010

10 9 8 7 6 5 4 3 2 1